Crock: Here's Sand In Your Nose

Bill Rechin & Don Wilder

First published in 1986 by Ballantine Books
Coronet edition 1987

British Library C.I.P.

Rechin, Bill
Crock, here's sand in your nose.
I. Title II. Wilder, Don
741.5'973 PN6728.C7

ISBN 0 340 41116 3

Printed and bound in Great Britain for Hodder and Stoughton Paperbacks, a division of Hodder and Stoughton Ltd., Mill Road, Dunton Green, Sevenoaks, Kent (Editorial Office: 47 Bedford Square, London, WC1B 3DP) by Cox & Wyman Ltd., Reading.

WHOA, CAMEL!

HIS 'WHOA' NEEDS TO BE RECALLED
SCREECH

HAS CROCK GIVEN YOU A NEW JOB ASSIGNMENT YET?
NO...

BUT I'M SURE MY NEW ASSIGNMENT WILL REFLECT THE COMMANDANT'S OPINION OF MY VALUE TO HIM

ARE YOU ALLERGIC TO BUFFALO CHIPS?

BOOK MOBILE
THESE ROMANCE NOVELS REALLY REVVED ME UP

BABY, MY MOTOR IS A ROLLS-ROYCE

AND THE CHASSIS IS A DUNE BUGGY

I'VE DECIDED TO ENTER A MADONNA LOOK-ALIKE CONTEST
YOU'LL NEED A MOLE ON YOUR UPPER LIP

THAT'S JUST MY LUCK...

I CUT IT OFF THIS MORNING, SHAVING

THIS JOB AIN'T TAKING ME NOWHERE!

BOOM

YEAH IT IS... IT'S TAKING YOU CLOSE TO THE NATURAL GAS LINE

SIR, REMEMBER BEFORE YOU WENT ON VACATION YOU SAID IF ANY PROBLEM CAME UP, NO MATTER HOW SMALL...

TIMES ARE TOUGH, FIGOWITZ...
THIS IS ALL WE HAVE
I'M TIRED OF EATING OLD BOOTS!

YOU SPEND ALL DAY PLANNING A MEAL AND NO ONE APPRECIATES IT

IF THE ENEMY ATTACKS, YOUR JOB IS TO FIRE ON THEM

I AIN'T GOT NO BULLETS... WHAT CAN I USE?

BETTER ENGLISH

CAN'T YOU KEEP YOURSELF A LITTLE NEATER?
YOU MEAN I AIN'T NEAT?

YOU'RE THE ONLY PERSON I KNOW WHO LEAVES A RING AROUND A GLASS AFTER HE DRINKS OUT OF IT

WHAT MAKES IT DARK, BUFORD?

DARK BUGS

BOY, I WISH I HAD IT ALL TOGETHER LIKE YOU DO, BUFORD

WIGGLE
WIGGLE

KNOW WHO I'D LIKE TO MEET, CUTIE PIE?

A CHIROPRACTOR?

I CERTAINLY ENJOYED MY YOUTH...

I RAISED LITTLE BUNNIES AS A BOY

WHAT DID YOU RAISE, SIR?
WHARF RATS

I WANT A VOLUNTEER WHO HAS NEVER FLINCHED IN THE FACE OF BATTLE

THEN DO WE HAVE ANYONE WITH ONLY ONE FLINCH?

WE'RE DOOMED! BUT THERE'S SOMETHING I WANT YOU TO KNOW...

I PUT YOU IN FOR THE LOYALTY MEDAL
THAT'S SWELL, LEO...

MAKES ME WISH I'D NEVER SOLD OUR TOP SECRETS

I'M ESCAPING TOMORROW
WHAT'S YOUR PLAN?

I'LL DISGUISE MYSELF AS A DINOSAUR
THEY'RE EXTINCT

BOY, I WISH I HAD YOUR KNACK FOR DETAIL

LIGHT THE FUSE AND RUN INTO THE FORT

I CAN'T RUN... I'VE GOT A BAD HEART

OKAY, THEN WALK
THAT'S MORE LIKE IT

THESE LONG EYELASHES ARE GREAT FOR KEEPING SAND OUT OF YOUR EYES

... NOT SO GREAT FOR GOING INTO A LONGSHOREMAN'S BAR FOR A BEER
BAR
WHISTLE

WHAT A LOUSY PLACE!
IT'S AWFUL IN THESE HOTBOXES

YOU GUYS SHOULDN'T COMPLAIN...

THAT'S THE WAY WE HAD TO DRESS IN MY OLD NEIGHBORHOOD TO GO OUT

FEATHERS
IT'S LIKE THEY SAY, HARRY, IT'S WHO YOU KNOW IN LIFE THAT COUNTS

WHAT'S NEW, GROSSIE?
I HAVE A CUTE JOKE TO TELL YOU

GREAT... I HAVEN'T HAD A GOOD LAUGH...

SINCE YOU TOLD ME A SIZE TEN DRESS JUST HANGS ON YOU

FOR THE LAST TIME, DARYL...
YOU **DON'T** 'HIGH FIVE' ANY BROTHER WHO WORKS IN THE GRENADE SHED

A PENNY FOR YOUR THOUGHTS, VERN
I WAS THINKING OF SAND
OUTPOST
5

WHATEVER MADE YOU THINK OF SAND?
JUST ONE OF THOSE CRAZY THINGS THAT POP INTO YOUR MIND
5

WHY DO YOU DIG ALL THOSE HOLES ?

BECAUSE I'M INTO HOLES
HAR HAR

I SHOULD HAVE SEEN THAT ONE COMING

SAND AND HEAT I CAN TAKE... BUT I HATE CLIMBING STAIRS

CAMEL
WASH

I STILL THINK IT WAS MORE FUN BEFORE THE ARMS REDUCTION TREATY

POOR KROUSE... HE HAD NERVES OF STEEL AND A HEART OF IRON

WAS HE KILLED IN BATTLE?

HE GOT HIT BY LIGHTNING

I'M GONNA REDUCE YOUR FORT TO A 'HANDYMAN'S SPECIAL'

GEEZE, EVERY-BODY MUST BE IN REAL ESTATE NOWADAYS

WHAT'S THAT?

A CHINESE CARRY-OUT

HEY, FIG, THE LEGION IS STARTING A SOFTBALL TEAM, WANNA PLAY?
SURE, SOFTBALL IS ONE THING I REALLY KNOW

O.K. MAN, WHAT POSITION DO YOU PLAY?

FOURTH BASE

I LIKE A MAN WHO CAN QUICKLY GRASP WHAT I'M SAYING, POULET

THAT'S ME, SIR... IF IT'S A FAST GRASPER YOU WANT, NOBODY CAN GRASP FASTER THAN ME, IN FACT...

WHAT'S WRONG?
I GOT KICKED IN THE GRASPER

WHAT'S WRONG?
I'VE LOST FOUR PET GOLDFISH THIS WEEK...

I DON'T UNDERSTAND IT...

I CHANGE THEIR SAND EVERY DAY

SHAME ON YOU, GROSSIE, FOR LOSING YOUR FIGURE!
CANDY

LET'S FACE IT

SOME OF US ARE BUN-BUN GIRLS...

AND SOME OF US ARE BON-BON GIRLS

SOMETIMES I'M SUSPICIOUS OF THE BEEF CROCK BUYS FOR US
WHY?

MY MEATLOAF JUST JUMPED UP AND CAUGHT A FRISBEE

IF YOU SAY 'IT IS WRITTEN IN THE SAND' ONE MORE TIME I'M GONNA BREAK YOUR FACE

IT'S BEEN TEN LONG, HOT MISERABLE YEARS SINCE YOU GOT US LOST!

THE MEN ARE PLANNING TO HANG YOU!

WELL, THIS CERTAINLY IS A FAR CRY FROM THE USUAL SUGGESTION BOX COMPLAINT

YOU'RE LUCKY THE MEN DIDN'T HANG YOU

NO DOUBT THE THOUGHT OF DOING HARM TO THEIR BELOVED LEADER BROUGHT TEARS TO THEIR EYES

NO, WE LOST THE ROPE

ANY SIGN OF THE LOST PATROL, POULET?
I'VE JUST LOCATED THEM

WHERE DID THE CIRCLES COME FROM?
I DON'T KNOW.. BUT THEY'RE FUN TO TOUCH

I DON'T HAVE ENOUGH COURAGE TO CAPTURE THAT HILL
NONSENSE... HITCH YOUR BELT UP HIGH AND CHARGE!

WHAT DID WE CAPTURE TODAY, OMAR?
SOME LEGION JOKER IN SHORT PANTS RUNNING TIPPY TOES

WILL THERE BE ANY 'LEFTOVERS' AFTER THE BATTLE, SIR?

THE MILITARY TERM IS 'SURVIVORS,' FARNSWORTH

BOOM
HOW DO YOU FEEL ABOUT LIVING IN A DUPLEX, BUFORD?

YOU LOOK MAAAARVELOUS!

I COULDN'T RESIST THAT

ONCE WE FIGURE OUT WHAT 'RR' MEANS I THINK THE REST OF THE PUZZLE WILL FALL INTO PLACE
RR
J

UNTIL MY PET RAT IS FOUND YOU'LL NEVER GET OUT!
OUR HEARTFELT SYMPATHY IS WITH YOU, SIR
3·28
HE CERTAINLY LOVES THAT RAT
THEY HAVE THE SAME MOTHER

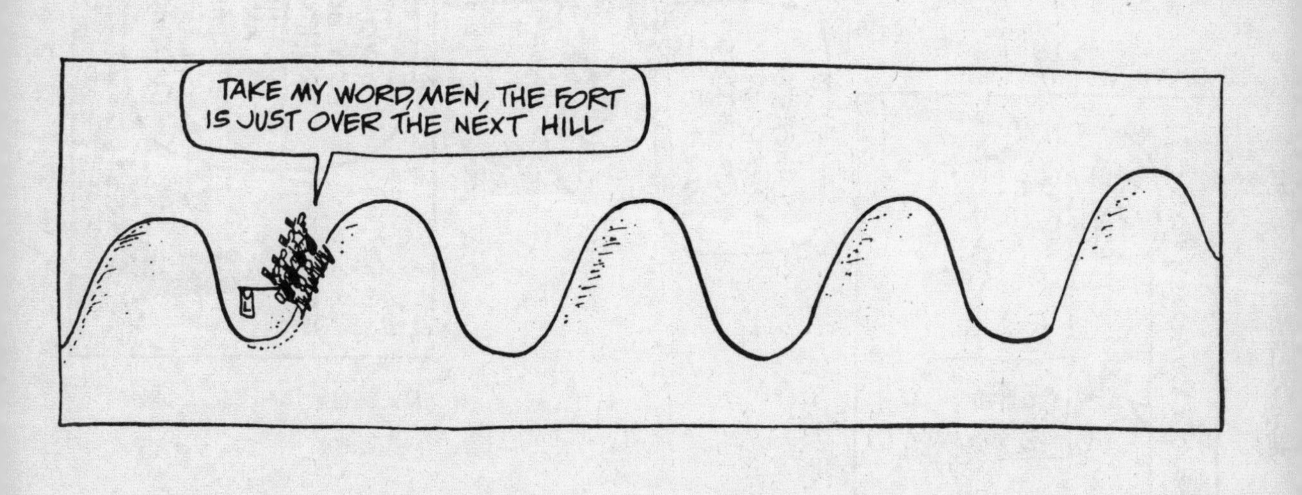
TAKE MY WORD, MEN, THE FORT IS JUST OVER THE NEXT HILL

WHERE ARE YOU GOING, VERN?
INTO TOWN TO SEE A MOVIE
OUTPOST 5

THERE'S **NO TOWN** AND THERE'S **NO MOVIE**

BOY, YOU SURE KNOW HOW TO THROW COLD WATER ON AN OTHERWISE GALA EVENING

ANY SCRAPS, SIR?
I FEED MY LEFTOVERS TO THE CATS

I GOTTA LEARN TO PURR

WHY DIDN'T WE STOP AT THE LAST RESTAURANT ?

THAT RESTAURANT HAD NO TRUCKS

WHO EATS TRUCKS ?

I NEED A MEDIC
WHERE DID YOU GET HIT?

YOU KNOW THE 'FRUIT OF THE LOOM' SHORTS I WEAR?
YES

I GOT SHOT IN THE PINEAPPLE

I'M THE KIND OF A LEADER WHO NEVER TAKES NO FOR AN ANSWER
NO KIDDING

NOW CUT THAT OUT!

I CAN'T BELIEVE IT... I WALKED UNDER A LADDER WITHOUT BAD LUCK

WELCOME, RECRUITS...

IN THE LEGION YOU'LL EAT SAND, FIGHT BARBARIANS AND DIE A LONELY DEATH IN SOME FORSAKEN OUTPOST

I GUESS THAT SQUASHES THE IDEA OF COMMUTING

POOR MALCOLM JUST GOT HIT WITH A 400-POUND CANNONBALL
WHAT'S HIS CONDITION?
© News America Syndicate, 1985

WELL, I'D SAY HE'S A LITTLE MOODY RIGHT NOW

YOUR REPORT ON BATTLEFIELD DEFENSES WAS SUPERB, CAPTAIN PREPPIE

WHAT DO YOU THINK OF MY REPORT, SIR?

WHAT'S WRONG WITH QUENCH?

HE JUST FOUND AGE SPOTS ON HIS HUMP

DID YOU TELL MAGGOT TO PLANT MY ROSE BUSH?
YES, SIR

DID YOU TELL HIM EXACTLY WHAT SIZE TO MAKE THE HOLE?
SIR...

GIVE THE GUY SOME CREDIT

THAT'S THE DOCTOR
WHO'S **ALWAYS** TELLING
ME TO LOSE WEIGHT

THEN YOU KNOW WHAT
YOU MUST DO
I
CERTAINLY
DO

FIND A
FAT
DOCTOR

YOU'RE GETTING OLD, QUENCH, YOUR HUMP IS SAGGING

I WONDER IF I CAN GET A HUMP-LIFT?

WHY DOES CROCK ALWAYS FAVOR YOU OVER ME?

BECAUSE I'M COMPETENT, HIGHLY MOTIVATED, AGGRESSIVE AND EXTREMELY INGENIOUS

DON'T GO AWAY, THERE'S MORE

I DONT WANT ANY JOKES ABOUT MY NOSE THIS HALLOWEEN
YOU HAVE MY WORD, THERE'LL BE NO STUPID REMARKS

YOU KNOW, I REALLY **LIKE** THAT GUY

I LOVE YOU TOO, PUMPKIN NOSE!

BOOK
MOBILE
WHO'S THAT?

THAT'S MR. ████████
OUR BOOK CENSOR

IT AIN'T FAIR MAKING ME DIG SALT IN YOUR MINES

OKAY, FROM NOW ON... YOU'RE A SODIUM CHLORIDE EXTRACTOR

THAT'S MORE LIKE IT

(SIGH☆) EVERYONE KNOWS I'M A FAILURE...
AT LEAST THIS TINY BUG DOESN'T KNOW OR CARE
FAILURE
I HATE INFORMED BUGS

ARE YOU SURE YOU KNOW HOW TO RIDE QUENCH?
HEY, MAN, I'M AN EXPERT ON CAMEL RIDING

WELL... WHADDYA WAITING FOR?
HOW DO YOU PUT THE TOP UP IF IT STARTS RAINING?

YOU'RE A LOW-LIFE SCUZZBALL, CROCK!
MUMPHH... MUMPHHP.... MUMPHHH!

I LOVE TO CATCH HIM DURING LUNCH TIME
MUMPH!... MUMPHH!

IN THE LEGION YOU'LL BE ABUSED, WORK LONG HOURS AND BE UNDERPAID
JOIN THE LEGION

WHY WOULD A SCHOOLTEACHER WANT THIS JOB?

WHEN YOU GET A CHANCE FOR ADVANCEMENT, YOU TAKE IT.

SIR, I'VE DISCOVERED A CUNNING WAY TO SIGNAL FOR HELP

I'LL REFLECT THE SUN IN THIS MIRROR
WHAT IF IT'S A RAINY DAY?

THAT'S SIMPLE... I'LL WEAR A RAINCOAT

'GO'

THAT WAS MY POWER PLAY FOR THE DAY

YOU'RE SUPPOSED TO WALK ON THE **OUTSIDE**

GIVE ME TEN BAGS OF GOLD OR I'LL ATTACK YOU, CROCK!

TEN BAGS... THAT'S OUTRAGEOUS!
IT COULD BE WORSE, SIR...
11-22

HE COULD'VE ASKED US TO GIVE HIM WHAT WE PAY FOR CAR INSURANCE EACH YEAR

GOODNIGHT, SIR.
GOODNIGHT, POULET..

A NIGHT LIKE THIS MAKES ME THINK OF HOW EXOTIC AND ADVENTUROUS THE LEGION IS

WHAT DOES IT MAKE YOU THINK ABOUT, SIR?
SAND FLEAS

SMOKING
NON-SMOKING

I'D LIKE SOMETHING WITH NO VIOLENCE AND NO SEX
BOOK MOBILE

WHAT DID HE GIVE YOU?
A BOOK OF WALLPAPER SAMPLES

DID YOU ENJOY THE THANKSGIVING CRUMB I GAVE YOU, FIGOWITZ?
I SENT IT TO THE HUNGRY PEOPLE IN AFRICA

WHAT THE HECK, PEANUT BUTTER AND CRANBERRY SAUCE AIN'T SO BAD
TO AFRICA

THE MEN LOOK TOO HAPPY,... THEY NEED TO BE HARASSED

SIR, DON'T YOU SEE SOMETHING WRONG IN WHAT YOU'RE DOING?
I CERTAINLY DO, POULET

THIS BABY NEEDS MORE LEAD IN THE PINKIE

WHEN LOOKS WERE HANDED OUT, YOU WERE AT THE HEAD OF THE LINE

I MUST'VE FORGOTTEN TO GET IN LINE

OUTPOST
5
I KNOW YOU'RE OUT THERE WAITING YOUR CHANCE

NO, WE'RE NOT
I'M WATCHING T.V.
ME TOO
I'M GETTING READY FOR BED
I'M READING A WESTERN
I'M WASHING MY HAIR
5

THEY WONT ATTACK TODAY, SIR
THEY WILL ATTACK TODAY

HOW CAN YOU BE SO SURE?
JUST LOOK AT THE NEXT PANEL

LISTEN... AIN'T THEY PLAYING OUR SONG?

WHACK

NEXT TIME DON'T FLUSH LIKE 'MOON RIVER'.

ALL RIGHT... WHO'S THE WISE GUY WHISTLING '♪ MR. SANDMAN... SEND ME A DREAM ♪'

FOR PUNISHMENT YOU'LL MARCH 500 MILES WITH ROCKS IN YOUR PACKS
THAT AIN'T FAIR!

SO YOU THINK I'M UNJUST?

YEAH, HE'S GOT MORE ROCKS THAN ME

THIS PLACE USED TO BE FILLED WITH THE MEANEST, UGLIEST BUNCH OF PEOPLE I'VE EVER SEEN

WHERE DID THEY GO?

THEY WERE ALL HIRED TO MAKE T.V. ROCK VIDEOS

THE DEFENSE CONTRACTOR JUST DELIVERED OUR NEW MILITARY CLOCK, SIR

IT ONLY COST FOUR THOUSAND DOLLARS
IT DOESN'T HAVE AN HOUR HAND ON IT!

HOW WAS I TO KNOW YOU WANTED THE PRECISION MODEL?

SIR, WHY ARE WE CALLED 'THE LOST PATROL'?

BECAUSE WE'VE BEEN LOST FOR TWENTY YEARS

BOY, THE PUBLIC IS SURE FAST TO STICK LABELS ON YOU

LITTLE DOES HE KNOW I'VE WRAPPED BOTH LEGS IN IRON SO HE CAN'T HURT ME

SPLOTCH

NICE TRY, 'RUSTY'

WHY DID CROCK TOSS YOU IN THERE?
I STOLE HIS HORSE AND ATE IT

WAS IT WITH MALICE?
NO, WITH MUSTARD

OH MIGHTY ONE...WHAT CAN I DO TO STAY YOUNG?
TAKE A DRINK OF MY MAGIC YOUTH POTION

DOES IT DO ANY GOOD?

IT SURE KEEPS THE MOSS OFF MY BOULDERS
HAR' HAR'

QUENCH WAS CAUGHT STEALING WATER
DO YOU HAVE ANY EVIDENCE?

ONLY CIRCUMSTANTIAL, YOUR HONOR

WHEN I ASK FOR AN INTELLIGENCE REPORT ON THE ENEMY'S CAMP, POULET...

I DON'T WANT IT DESCRIBED AS HAVING 'GOBS OF ATMOSPHERE'

I'VE RESOLVED NOT TO STEP ON YOUR LEG IN 1986, FIGOWITZ

I'D LIKE THE OPPORTUNITY TO SAY SOMETHING AT THIS TIME, SIR
CERTAINLY

YOU'RE STANDING ON MY PINKIE!

I HOPE YOU HAVEN'T PUT IN YOUR SPRING TOMATO PLANTS, SIR
ZZZZZZZZ

WHAT ARE YOU IN THE HOTBOX FOR?
D.W.D.

DRIVING WHILE DRUNK?

NO, DALLYLING WITH DOREEN

WE'VE ENTERED THE COMPUTER AGE, MEN...

THIS BABY WILL LEAD US TO THE FORT WHEN I PUT IN THE PROPER SOFTWARE

NOW WE'VE GOT A SOFTHEAD USING SOFTWARE

I'VE FED HOURS OF DATA INTO THIS MARVEL OF TECHNOLOGY, HAWTHORNE...
CRANK
CRANK

AND IN A SPLIT SECOND IT'LL TELL US WHERE THE FORT IS

CAN I BUY A VOWEL, PAT ?

OOOOH... A WHOLE GLASS OF WATER TO LAST ME FOR A WEEK... OH, GOLLY GEE, THANK YOU, SIR!

WE CAMELS ARE BORN TO ENDURE THE HARSH DESERT LIFE WITHOUT A WHIMPER

ANYONE OUT THERE WANT TO WHIMPER FOR ME?

I'VE GOT TO LOSE A FEW POUNDS
WHAT MAKES YOU SAY THAT?

I'VE HAD TO BUY INDUSTRIAL STRENGTH PANTYHOSE THE LAST TWO TIMES

THE MEN ARE STARVING, YET THEY GO TO CHURCH

WHERE ELSE CAN YOU GET FREE CANDLES TO EAT?

THERE'S NOT MUCH HOPE BUT THERE IS ONE BRIGHT SPOT

WE'RE SMARTER THAN THEY ARE
THAT WON'T WORK...

THEY'VE ALREADY SEEN YOU

TROOPER BENSON RACED A TRAIN TO THE CROSSING AFTER HE'D BEEN DRINKING LAST NIGHT

WHO USUALLY WINS THOSE RACES?

CAN YOU EVER RECALL SEEING A LOCOMOTIVE BEING BURIED?

THIS IS A LETTER FROM MY BROTHER, THE FAMOUS WRITER

HIS WORK IS READ THE WORLD OVER
REALLY, WHAT DID HE WRITE?

'BATTERIES NOT INCLUDED'

IT'S HOPELESS, MEN... THE ENEMY HAS US BOXED IN

TRIP

WHY CAN'T YOU DO ANYTHING RIGHT, FIGOWITZ ?
2.3

MAYBE I WAS THE WORLD'S FIRST TEST-TUBE BLOOPER

DO YOU ENJOY WATCHING TV ?
WATCHING TOO MUCH TV WILL TURN YOUR BRAIN TO MUSH

IN YOUR CASE, WHY FIGHT PROGRESS?
?

I HEAR YOUR ENTIRE FAMILY WERE DOUBLE-AGENT SPIES
YEAH, BUT IT WAS TERRIBLE

NOBODY KNEW WHICH TOOTHBRUSH TO USE

WANNA HELP ME GIVE CROCK HIS BIRTHDAY PRESENT?
SURE

DARN!
DID YOU FORGET THE CARD?

NO, THE FUSE

WHAT WAS YOUR LATEST ESCAPE ATTEMPT?

I TRIED THE 'HONEY BEE' DISGUISE
THAT SOUNDS CLEVER

NOT WHEN YOUR STINGER BRUSHES AGAINST A HIGH VOLTAGE POLE

NOW
AYING
BOY, THAT MOVIE HAD SOME GREAT LOVE SCENES IN IT
YEAH, I COULD TELL THE PARTS YOU LIKED...

YOUR POPCORN STARTED POPPING AGAIN

CROSS
BRIDGE
WHEN
YOU GET
TO IT

WANNA JOIN OUR BASKETBALL TEAM, FIGOWITZ ?

AT LAST!... I'M ACCEPTED!!

I GET SO DISGUSTED... I CAN EAT AND EAT AND **NEVER** GAIN WEIGHT
2·21

WHAT'S ALL THE COMMOTION ?
SOME WOMAN GOT HIT IN THE FACE WITH A CHOCOLATE CREAM PIE
SWEET SHOPPE

ISN'T THE DESERT VILLAGE A QUIET AND SERENE PLACE?
Z
Z

EXCEPT DURING COMMERCIALS
FLUSH
FLUSH
FLUSH

YOU'VE GOT BREATH LIKE A BAG FULL OF OLIVE PITS!
GO SOAP A ROPE!

SIR, A PHONE CALL FOR YOU

DIDN'T I TELL YOU NOT TO BOTHER ME DURING THE PEACE TALKS?

DID YOU GO TO SPY SCHOOL?
MY MAJOR WAS INTERROGATION

I GOT A DEGREE IN THIRD

ONE PIECE OF ADVICE...

NEVER JUMP START YOUR CAMEL

I'D LIKE THE SMOKING SECTION

I'D LIKE THE NON-SMOKING SECTION

I'D LIKE THE HANDSOME SECTION

DRESS
SHOPPE

WHAT DO YOU
THINK I'D LOOK LIKE
IN SEQUINS?

JOHN MADDEN WITH
RUNNING LIGHTS

SIR, THE PENSION FUND IS SHORT!
THAT'S NO PROBLEM
3.10

STRETCH

HOW WOULD YOU DESCRIBE MY MILITARY CAREER, SIR?
PEE WEE AND HIS SANDBOX

HE CERTAINLY HAS A WAY WITH WORDS

THE DOCTOR JUST GAVE ME A LOW-STARCH DIET TO LOSE WEIGHT

WHAT DID HE RECOMMEND FOR YOU?

A LOW-FOOD DIET

DO YOU SUPPOSE THIS WILL AFFECT OUR MORTGAGE PAYMENTS?

DO YOU THINK I'M CONCEITED?
WHY SHOULD I THINK THAT?
BZZZZZz

DOESN'T EVERYONE'S ELECTRIC RAZOR PLAY 'PRETTY BABY' WHILE THEY SHAVE?

GOODBYE, LITTLE SISTER, I'M OFF TO SACK AND PLUNDER THE NOMADS

I SUPPOSE YOU'LL STEAL THEIR CROPS AND CATTLE

ARE YOU KIDDING?... WE GO FOR THE VCR's, STEREOS AND TAPE DECKS

AREN'T YOU FLYING YOUR CARPET TO WORK?
THERE'S A BIG TRAFFIC TIE-UP THIS MORNING

THE RADIO SAID IT WAS WALL-TO-WALL

PARKING
IN
REAR
ONLY
9.19

HOW ELSE WOULD I PARK IT?